EVERYDAY LIFE IN THE
MAYA
CIVILIZATION

KIRSTEN HOLM

PowerKiDS
press

New York

Published in 2012 by The Rosen Publishing Group, Inc.
29 East 21st Street, New York, NY 10010

First Edition

Editor: Joanne Randolph

Book Design: Planman Technologies

Illustrations: Planman Technologies

Library of Congress Cataloging-in-Publication Data

Holm, Kirsten C. (Kirsten Campbell)

Everyday life in the Maya civilization / by Kirsten Campbell Holm. — 1st ed.

   p. cm. — (Jr. graphic ancient civilizations)

Includes index.

ISBN 978-1-4488-6217-7 (library binding) — ISBN 978-1-4488-6393-8 (pbk.) — ISBN 978-1-4488-6394-5 (6-pack)

1. Mayas—Juvenile literature. 2. Mayas—Social life and customs—Juvenile literature. 3. Civilization, Ancient—Juvenile literature. I. Title.

F1435.H65 2012

972.81'01—dc23

                              2011027121

Manufactured in the United States of America

CPSIA Compliance Information: Batch #PLW2102PK: For Further Information contact
Rosen Publishing, New York, New York at 1-800-237-9932.

Contents

Historical Overview

- The Maya civilization spanned about 2,000 years, beginning around 1100 BC and ending in the early AD 1500s. Its history is divided into time periods.

- The Classic Period of the Maya civilization lasted about 600 years, from AD 250 until AD 900.

- The Maya civilization covered about 12,500 square miles (32,375 sq km) of land. Mayan lands included modern-day El Salvador, western Honduras, Guatemala, Belize, and parts of southern Mexico. Millions of descendants of the Maya still live in this region.

- Most Mayan lands were covered in forest, and active volcanoes are near places where the Maya lived.

- The Maya did not have one king. They had local rulers, and local leaders formed the ruling class.

- Almost all Mayan records were destroyed by the Spanish in the 1500s.

EVERYDAY LIFE IN THE
MAYA CIVILIZATION

AD 250, COPÁN, IN PRESENT-DAY HONDURAS

MOST OF WHAT WE KNOW ABOUT THE MAYA COMES FROM **EXCAVATIONS** OF THEIR CITIES AND VILLAGES. THE MAYA HAD LARGE FAMILIES, AND SEVERAL **GENERATIONS** OF ONE FAMILY LIVED TOGETHER.

THE MAYA THOUGHT THAT LONG, SLOPING FOREHEADS AND CROSSED EYES WERE A SIGN OF BEAUTY.

WHY DID YOU HANG THAT BEAD IN FRONT OF THE BABY'S EYES?

WHEN SHE LOOKS AT THE BEAD, IT WILL MAKE HER EYES CROSS. THE BOARDS WILL GIVE HER HEAD A BEAUTIFUL SHAPE.

WEALTHY MAYA LIVED IN HOMES MADE OF STONE BLOCKS. HOMES HAD **SHRINES** TO THEIR GODS, OUTDOOR KITCHENS, STOREROOMS, CHICKEN COOPS, AND GARDENS WHERE THEY GREW CORN, BEANS, AND SQUASH.

I AM GLAD YOU ARE UP EARLY. HELP ME PUT AWAY THESE SLEEPING MATS.

YOU KNOW I ALWAYS GET UP BEFORE DAWN SINCE THERE IS SO MUCH WORK TO DO.

THE MAYA WERE DEEPLY RELIGIOUS, AND THEY WORSHIPED MANY GODS. THEY BELIEVED THAT THEIR HOUSEHOLD GODS WOULD WATCH OVER THEM.

YOU MUST REMEMBER TO BEGIN THE DAY BY HONORING OUR GODS AND PRAYING FOR OUR SAFETY.

THE MAYA BATHED FREQUENTLY IN COLD WATER, AND SWEAT BATHS WERE PART OF THEIR **CEREMONIES** AND **RITUALS.** BATHS WERE IN HUTS SEPARATE FROM THE MAIN HOUSES.

LET'S BEGIN OUR DAY WITH A SWEAT BATH. IT WILL HELP PURIFY US.

MAYAN WOMEN DID ALL THE COOKING AND CLEANING. THEY GOT UP EARLY TO START THE KITCHEN FIRE AND PREPARE MEALS.

WOMEN DID LAUNDRY AT COMMUNITY FOUNTAINS CALLED *PILAS* OR IN NEARBY RIVERS. WOMEN ALSO WOVE CLOTH AND MADE CLOTHES FOR THEIR FAMILIES.

MY MOTHER DOES NOT READ OR WRITE.

YOU ARE A GOOD STUDENT. YOU COULD BECOME A **SCRIBE**.

I AM GLAD MOTHER TAUGHT ME HOW TO WEAVE.

THEY EXPECT US TO LEARN SO MUCH HERE.

THESE BOWLS WILL BE USEFUL WHEN WE ARE MARRIED.

THESE LESSONS ARE CERTAINLY NOT THE SAME AS THOSE MY BROTHER IS LEARNING IN THE HOUSE OF MEN!

AT ABOUT AGE 14, BOYS FROM NOBLE FAMILIES WENT TO LIVE IN COMMUNAL DORMITORIES, CALLED HOUSES OF MEN. BOYS LEARNED CRAFTS, GAMES, HOW TO BE WARRIORS, AND HOW TO DO THEIR CAREERS. DURING THE DAY, BOYS COULD JOIN THEIR FATHERS AT WORK.

YOU MUST LEARN TO FIGHT WITH COURAGE.

YOUNG MEN WHO WERE INTERESTED IN TRADE AND COMMERCE STUDIED WITH MATHEMATICIANS AND SCRIBES.

COUNT CAREFULLY. MAKE SURE YOUR NUMBERS ARE CLEARLY WRITTEN.

MY FATHER IS A PRIEST. I AM STUDYING TO BE A PRIEST, TOO.

I WANT TO BE A SCRIBE TO THE KING.

I THINK I WILL WALK THROUGH THE PLAZA ON THE WAY TO WORK. I MAY EVEN SEE MY SON AT THE PALACE TODAY.

THE GODS PREDICTED THAT WE WOULD FINISH THIS TEMPLE IN THREE YEARS. THE WORK IS GOING WELL.

AS I PRAYED AT HOME THIS MORNING. THE PRIESTS PRAYED HERE FOR OUR SAFETY AND THE COMPLETION OF THIS TEMPLE.

AT THE MARKET, PEOPLE EXCHANGED NEWS. CRAFTSMEN, ARTISTS, AND MERCHANTS SOLD THEIR GOODS. COCOA BEANS, JADE BEADS, AND SEASHELLS WERE USED AS MONEY.

I AM GLAD TO SEE YOU HERE. THERE ARE TRADERS WITH GOODS FROM THE COAST AND THE NORTH.

I HOPE YOU FIND SOME GOOD DEALS. I MUST HURRY TO WORK.

SCRIBES WERE SOMETIMES SENT TO LOOK AT THE HARVEST AND DECIDE HOW MUCH TRIBUTE FARMERS WOULD HAVE TO PAY TO THE KING. THE MAYA DID NOT HAVE HORSES OR DONKEYS. THEY WALKED OR WERE CARRIED IN SPECIAL CHAIRS.

WE NEED TO SEE HOW BAD THIS HARVEST IS.

WE HAD RAIN THIS YEAR. PERHAPS THEY DID NOT TAKE GOOD CARE OF THE FIELDS.

WE PLANTED WHEN THE PRIESTS TOLD US. WE PRAYED FOR A GOOD HARVEST.

IF YOU DID AS THE PRIESTS SAID, YOUR CROPS WOULD NOT HAVE FAILED.

PRIESTS CONDUCTED BLOOD **SACRIFICES** TO MAKE THE GODS HAPPY SO THAT PEOPLE WOULD HAVE GOOD FORTUNE AND GOOD CROPS.

THIS IS A MUCH WORSE HARVEST THAN I EXPECTED. THE PEOPLE WHO LIVE IN THIS VILLAGE MAY STARVE.

CITY PEOPLE WILL NOT BE ABLE TO BUY FOOD EITHER.

WE MUST PRAY FOR RAIN AND CONDUCT THE PROPER CEREMONY WITH A BLOOD SACRIFICE.

THIS WILL SHOW THE GODS WE ARE SORRY.

SINCE RELIGION WAS SO IMPORTANT TO THE MAYA, PRIESTS WERE HIGHLY RESPECTED. PRIESTS STUDIED ASTRONOMY TO FIND OUT THE WILL OF THE GODS. THEY ALSO ORGANIZED RELIGIOUS FESTIVALS.

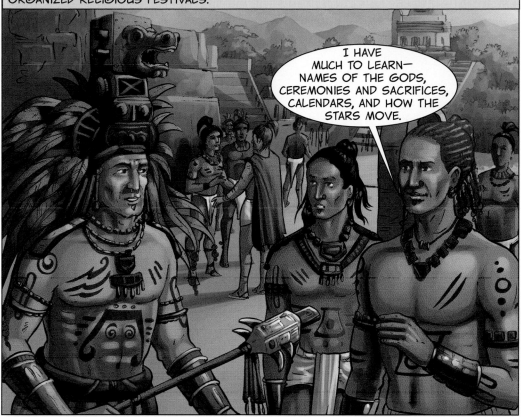

MULUC NEW YEAR CELEBRATIONS WERE LIVELY EVENTS. THE GOD MULUC WAS ASSOCIATED WITH GOOD HARVESTS, RAIN, AND FERTILITY.

THE FIRE DANCE WAS JUST ONE OF THE DANCES PERFORMED DURING THE MULUC CELEBRATION. RATTLESNAKES WERE OFTEN SEEN ON DECORATIONS AT MULUC CELEBRATIONS.

THE MAYA BELIEVED THAT THE RATTLESNAKE WAS A SACRED ANIMAL THAT SENT OUT RAIN AND SUN FROM ITS FANGS.

THE MULUC CELEBRATION WAS FANTASTIC. WE CAN ALL GO TO THE BALL COURTS THIS AFTERNOON.

I LOVE *POK-TA-POK.* I WONDER WHICH TEAM WILL WIN.

POK-TA-POK WAS PLAYED WITH A LARGE, HARD RUBBER BALL. PLAYERS COULD HIT THE BALL WITH THEIR HIPS, KNEES, ELBOWS, AND ARMS. THEY COULD NOT USE THEIR HANDS OR FEET.

THE MAYA BELIEVED THAT BECAUSE THE GODS HAD GIVEN THEM SO MUCH, HUMANS HAD TO GIVE THEIR LIVES IN THANKS. THIS WAS THE **FATE** OF THE LOSING TEAM.

THE PLAYERS ARE DRESSED AS IF THEY WERE GOING INTO BATTLE.

IT IS A TOUGH GAME.

IT WENT THROUGH THE RING. THEY WON!

YOU WILL PAY FOR YOUR LOSS WITH YOUR LIFE. IT IS AN HONOR, A GIFT TO THE GODS.

Did You Know?

- Mayan writing was based on hieroglyphics and had more than 800 symbols.

- Mayan society was divided into groups. At the top was the ruling class, followed by priests, and then craftsmen, who built houses and furniture and made clothing. At the bottom were common people, including farmers, hunters, soldiers, and laborers.

- Mayan men wore their hair long. Short hair was a sign that a man was a criminal.

- The Maya believed that the world was created by more than one god, and they worshiped many gods.

- The Maya had two principal calendars. The first calendar was divided into 365 days. It had 18 months of 20 days each. The remaining five days were considered unlucky days, and the Maya did not work on those days. The second calendar had 260 days. It was used to plan daily activities, for example to decide which days would be good for planting crops, traveling, or for marriage.

  The Mayans used a third calendar as well. This third calendar was a lunar calendar that they used for planting and harvesting.

Glossary

accurate (A-kyuh-rut) Exactly right.

appease (uh-PEEZ) To satisfy or to bring peace.

ceremonies (SER-ih-moh-neez) Special series of actions done on certain occasions.

descendants (dih-SEN-dents) People who are born of a certain family or group.

excavations (ek-skuh-VAY-shunz) Digging up things that were buried.

fate (FAYT) An outcome that cannot be changed.

generations (jeh-nuh-RAY-shunz) People who were born in the same period.

interpret (in-TER-prit) To explain the meaning.

predicted (prih-DIKT-ed) Made a guess based on facts or knowledge.

rituals (RIH-choo-ulz) Special series of actions done for reasons of faith.

sacrifice (SA-kruh-fys) Something that has been given up for a belief.

scribe (SKRYB) A person whose job is to copy books by hand.

shrines (SHRYNZ) Special places at which prayers or memorials can be made.

tally (TA-lee) A count.

Index

Web Sites

Due to the changing nature of Internet links, PowerKids Press has developed an online list of Web sites related to the subject of this book. This site is updated regularly. Please use this link to access the list:

www.powerkidslinks.com/civi/maya/